SPMG

S H M | I

Scottish Heinemann Maths

Check-ups

Name _____

Colour 3 red.   Colour 2 blue.

1 and 1   1 add 2   3 add 0

2 + 0   2 + 1   0 + 4   0 + 3

Make 5.

   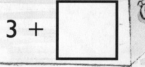   

4 + ☐   ☐ + 4   3 + ☐   ☐ + 5

3 and 1 = ☐   1 add 0 = ☐   2 add 2 = ☐

5 + 0 = ☐   1 + 3 = ☐   0 + 1 = ☐

3 + ☐ = 5   ☐ + 0 = 4   0 + ☐ = 2

3 + 2 + 0 = ☐   1 + 1 + 2 = ☐   1 + 3 + 1 = ☐

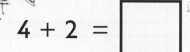

4 + 2 = ☐   1 + 6 = ☐   3 + 3 = ☐

4 + 3 = ☐   6 + 0 = ☐   5 + 2 = ☐

3 + 4 = ☐   0 + 7 = ☐   1 + 5 = ☐

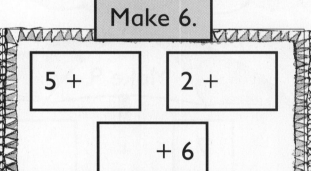

Make 6.

5 +   2 +

    + 6

Make 7.

7 +   + 1

        + 5

Colour [6] red.   Colour [7] blue.

3 add 4	1 add 6	4 and 2	0 and 7
4 + 3	1 add 5	5 add 2	0 + 6
1 + 2 + 3	2 add 4	5 + 1	3 + 3 + 1

Tick (✓) three ◯ to make 6.   Tick (✓) three ◯ to make 7.

① ④ ② ③   ① ⑤ ③ ① ②

6 + 2 =

2 + 7 =

8 + 1 =

9 + 0 =

4 + 4 =

1 + 7 =

5 + 2 =

6 + 3 =

0 + 8 =

2 + 6 =

4 + 5 =

3 + 3 =

Make 8.

Make 9.

3 add ☐

☐ + ☐

☐ add 1

7 + ☐

☐ add 4

☐ add ☐

1 + 2 + 6 =

1 + 4 + 3 =

1 + 7 + 0 =

0 + 1 + 8 =

9 + 1 = ☐   6 add 2 = ☐   5 + 5 = ☐

2 + 7 = ☐   10 add 0 = ☐   7 + 3 = ☐

8 + ☐ = 10

3 + ☐ = 9

0 + ☐ = 10

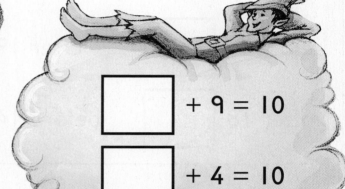

☐ + 9 = 10

☐ + 4 = 10

Colour  .

3 add 7   4 + 6   2 + 4 + 3

1 + 8   3 + 4 + 1   2 add 8

Tick (✔) two 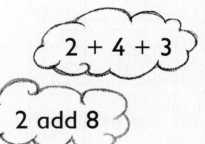 to make 10.

1   7   2   3

Tick (✔) three 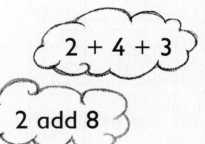 to make 10.

2   1   2   6   3

Write the missing numbers.

| 16 | 17 | | |

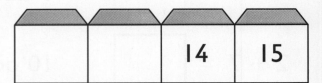

| | | 14 | 15 |

Write the number

before 11 [ ]   after 19 [ ]   before 16 [ ]

after 18 [ ]   before 14 [ ]   after 17 [ ]

Match

the number

after 11

after 13

after 15

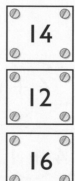

14

12

16

the number

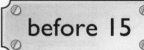

before 15

before 17

before 13

Write the number between

12 and 14 [ ]   13 and 15 [ ]

20 and 18 [ ]   16 and 14 [ ]

Write **one** number between 12 and 17. [ ]

Tick (✓) the larger number.

Tick (✓) the smaller number.

Colour the largest number.

Colour the smallest number.

Write the numbers in order.

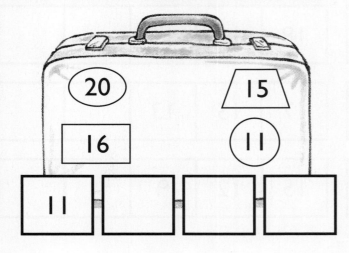

11			

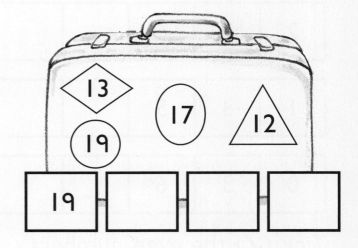

19			

1 more than 14 ➞ ☐

2 less than 19 ➞ ☐

2 less than 13 ➞ ☐

2 more than 10 ➞ ☐

2 more than 18 ➞ ☐

1 less than 15 ➞ ☐

Join in order. Colour.

16

18

20

14•

•9

12•

•6

4

2

8 6

15

18 •3

0

12 10

0

Write the missing numbers.

2	4	6		

18	16	14		

1	3	5		

17	15	13		

0	3	6		

15	12	9		

Tick (✓) the even numbers.

2   3   6   9   12   16   19

Tick (✓) the odd numbers.

1   4   7   9   11   14   20

Write the numbers.

nineteen ☐   eleven ☐   thirteen ☐

fifteen ☐   twenty ☐   fourteen ☐

Match.

17

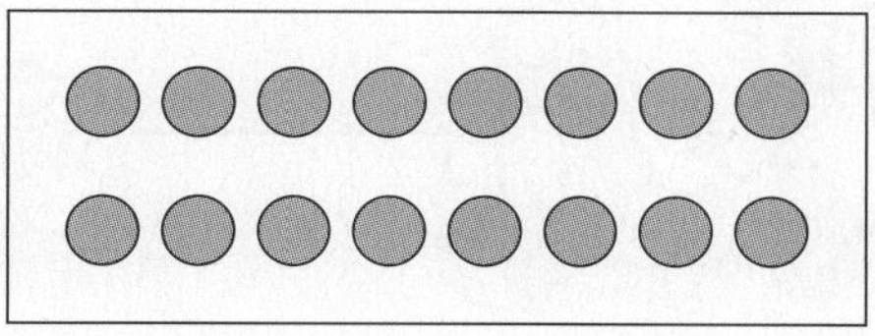

sixteen

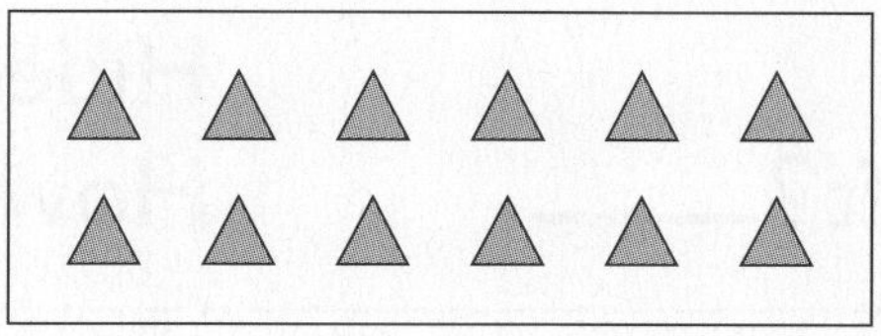

12

twelve

16

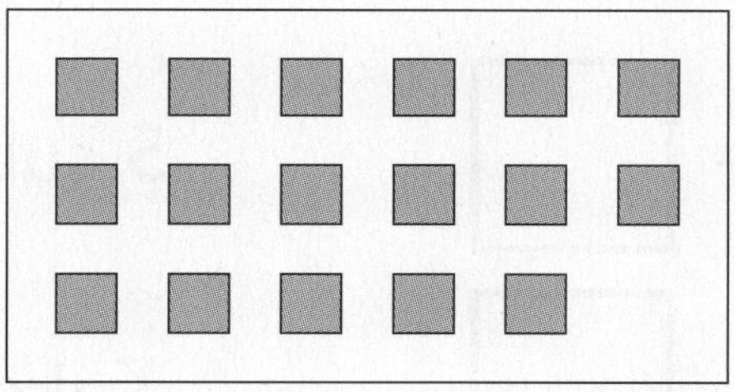

seventeen

Colour the **seventh** **3rd** **first** **9th** .

2 – 1 = ☐   4 – 4 = ☐   5 – 1 = ☐

4 – 3 = ☐   2 – 0 = ☐   5 – 5 = ☐

3 – 0 = ☐   3 – 2 = ☐   4 – 0 = ☐

Hide 2.
How many are left? _____

Hide 3.
How many are left? _____

4 less than 5 = ☐

5 subtract 0 = ☐

Subtract 1 from 3. ☐

Take 2 from 2. ☐

2 + 3 = ☐

3 + 2 = ☐

5 – 3 = ☐

5 – 2 = ☐

8 – 7 = ☐   8 – 2 = ☐   8 – 0 = ☐

7 – 1 = ☐   7 – 0 = ☐   7 – 3 = ☐

6 – 4 = ☐   6 – 1 = ☐   6 – 6 = ☐

8 – 3 = ☐   7 – 4 = ☐   6 – 5 = ☐

Match.

 8 – 6    7 – 2    6 – 3

6   4   2   3   5   0

 6 – 0    8 – 4    7 – 7

8 take away 5 = ☐   7 subtract 6 = ☐

Take 1 from 8. ☐   Take 2 from 6. ☐

Subtract 5 from 7. ☐   Subtract 5 from 6. ☐

9 − 5 = ☐

10 − 9 = ☐

9 − 0 = ☐

10 − 0 = ☐

9 − 7 = ☐

10 − 4 = ☐

9 − 8 = ☐

10 − 6 = ☐

9 − 9 = ☐

Match.

(9 − 7)   (10 − 8)   (10 − 5)   (9 − 9)   (9 − 2)

[2]   [8]   [0]   [5]   [7]

(10 − 2)   (10 − 10)   (9 − 1)   (10 − 3)   (9 − 4)

3 fly away.
How many are left? ☐

6 are sold.
How many are left? ☐

10 subtract 7 = ☐

6 less than 9 = ☐

9 take away 8 = ☐

Take 4 from 10. ☐

How many more ? _____

−	=

Find the difference between

2 and 8 _____   10 and 5 _____

Complete.

☐ − ☐ = 4   ☐ − ☐ = 0

3 + 6 =

6 + 3 =

9 − 3 =

9 − 6 =

5 + 2 = 7

+ 5 = 7

− 5 = 2

7 − ☐ = 5

6 − ☐ = 5   ☐ − 2 = 7

10 − ☐ = 8   ☐ − 4 = 4

1 Write the number

after 13 ☐   before 16 ☐

between 17 and 19 ☐ .

2 Write the numbers in order.

(15) (9) (20) (12) (16)

9 ___ ___ ___ ___ ___

3

2 + 5 = ☐   4 + 4 = ☐   5 + 3 = ☐

6 + 0 = ☐   2 + 3 = ☐   8 + 1 = ☐

4   Make 10.

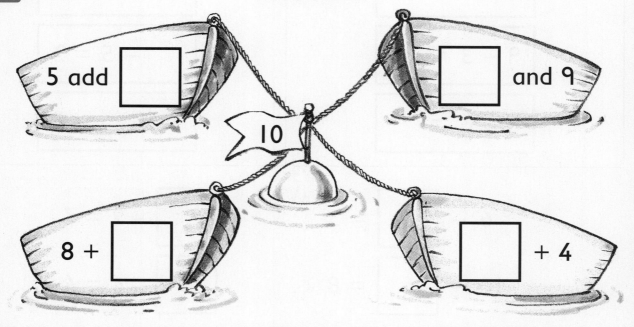

5 add ☐   ☐ and 9

10

8 + ☐   ☐ + 4

5   How many altogether?

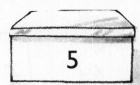 5   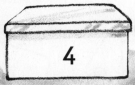 4   ☐

6

$7 - 3 =$ ☐ $10 - 5 =$ ☐ $9 - 8 =$ ☐

$5 - 2 =$ ☐ $6 - 4 =$ ☐ $8 - 5 =$ ☐

7

_____ balloons.
3 blow away.
How many are left? _____

| _ | = |

8

How many more ? _____

| _ | = |

9

$7 + 2 = 9$

$ + 7 = 9$

$ - 2 = 7$

$9 - = 2$

10 Make £1 less. Make £2 more.

11 Tick (✓) coins to buy.

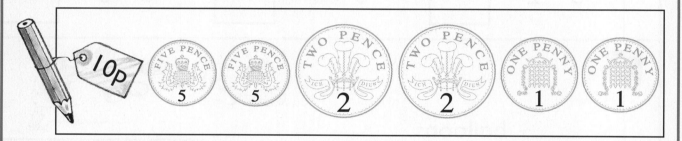

12 Match.

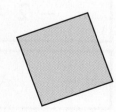

square

circle

triangle

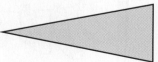

13 Draw a tall .   Draw a short .

14 Match.

6 o'clock

1 o'clock

11 o'clock

15 Sort the numbers. | ~~9~~   ~~5~~   10   2   6   8   7 |

less than 7	~~less than 7~~
5	9

1 Match.

| 14 | 12 | 20 | 15 |

twelve · fourteen · fifteen · twenty

2 Tick (✓) the 2nd and last .

3

7 + 3 = ☐   6 + 2 = ☐   1 + 8 = ☐

3 + 4 + 2 = ☐   1 + 5 + 4 = ☐

4

3 + ☐ = 8   ☐ add 2 = 9

5 + ☐ = 5   ☐ and 7 = 8

5 Make 6.

⬜ and ⬜

Make 7.

⬜ + ⬜ + ⬜

6

7 take away 6 = ⬜

2 less than 8 = ⬜

Subtract 0 from 9. ⬜

Take 4 from 10. ⬜

7 Find the difference between

2 and 10 ⬜

5 and 6 ⬜

8 and 1 ⬜

8

10

7 are sold.
How many are left? ——

⬜ – ⬜ = ⬜

9

9 – ⬜ = 3

⬜ – 5 = 0

10 – ⬜ = 10

⬜ – 3 = 1

10 How much?

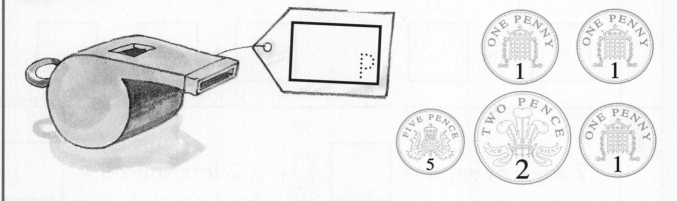

11 How much altogether?

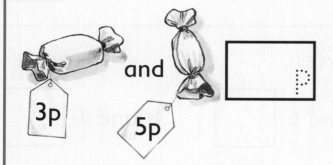 and [P]

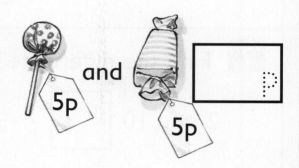 and [P]

$2p + 4p =$ [P] $6p + 3p =$ [P]

12

£7

Buy [scarf] £5

How much is left? [£]

$£8 - £6 =$ [£] $£10 - £7 =$ [£]

Sorting and matching

Sorting	PS 1	PS 2	PS 3	PS 4	PS 5	PS 6	PS 7	PS 8

Matching

Numbers to 10

One and two	PS 9

Three	PS 10	AB 1	AB 2	PS 11	AB 3

Four	PS 11	AB 4	AB 5	AB 6

Five	PS 12	AB 7	AB 8	AB 9

Ordering to 5	PS 13	AB 10	AB 11	AB 12

Six and seven	PS 14	PS 15	AB 13	AB 14	AB 15	AB 16

Eight and nine	PS 16	AB 17	AB 18	AB 19	AB 20

Ten	PS 17	AB 21	AB 22	AB 23

Ordering to 10	PS 17	AB 24	AB 25	PS 18	AB 26	PS 19	AB 27	PS 19	AB 28	AB 29

Numbers to 20

Patterns	AB 30	AB 31

Record of work: SHM 1

Addition to 10

Concept of addition

PS 20	AB 1	AB 2	PS 21	AB 3	AB 4

Recording addition

AB 5	PS 22	AB 6	AB 7

Adding 1 and 2

AB 8	AB 9

Addition facts to 5

AB 10	AB 11	AB 12

Consolidation of addition facts to 5

PS 22	AB 13

Assessment

AB 14

Addition to 5: consolidation

PS 23	PS 24	PS 25	AB 15	AB 16	HA 1	CU 1

Doubles and near doubles

PS 26	AB 17	PS 27	AB 18

Addition facts for 6 and 7

AB 19	AB 20	HA 2	AB 21	AB 22	PS 28	PS 29	PS 30	CU 2

Addition facts for 8 and 9

PS 30	AB 23	AB 24	HA 3	PS 30	PS 31	AB 25	AB 26	CU 3

Addition facts to 10

PS 32	AB 27	AB 28	AB 29	HA 4	CU 4

Assessment

AB 30	AB 31

Numbers to 20

Number sequence to 20

AB 1	AB 2	AB 3	AB 4	AB 5	AB 6	HA 5	CU 5

Counting to 20

PS 33	AB 7	AB 8	AB 9	PS 34	AB 10	HA 6

Comparing and ordering numbers

PS 35	PS 36	AB 11	AB 12	PS 37	AB 13	HA 7	AB 14	HA 8	CU 6

Even and odd numbers

PS 38	PS 39	AB 15	PS 38	PS 39	AB 16	PS 38	AB 17	HA 9	CU 7

Number names

AB 18	AB 19	AB 20	HA 10	CU 8

Ordinal numbers

Assessment

AB 21	AB 22	AB 23

Subtraction to 10

Concept of subtraction	AB 1	PS 40	AB 2

Subtraction involving 1, 2 and 0	AB 3	HA 11	AB 4

Subtraction facts to 5	AB 5	PS 41	AB 6	PS 42	AB 7	HA 12

Subtraction language	AB 8	HA 13	AB 9	AB 10	HA 14	AB 11	CU 9

Assessment	AB 12

Subtraction within 10	AB 13	HA 15	AB 14	AB 15	PS 43	AB 16	AB 17

Facts for 6 and 7	AB 18	HA 16	AB 19	AB 20	HA 17

Facts for 8 and 9	AB 21	AB 22	HA 18	CU 10	AB 23	AB 24	HA 19

Facts for 10	AB 25	AB 26	PS 44	HA 20	HA 21	AB 27	PS 45	CU 11

Subtraction: comparison	AB 28	AB 29	HA 22	PS 46	AB 30	PS 47

Linking + and − facts for 6 to 10	AB 31	AB 32	AB 33	AB 34	AB 35

Subtraction to 10	AB 36	AB 37	CU 12

Assessment	AB 38	AB 39

Money

Recognising coins	PS 48

Addition to 10p/£10	AB 1	PS 49	PS 50	AB 2	AB 3

Subtraction within 10p/£10	AB 4	AB 5	AB 6

Using 1p, 2p and 5p coins	PS 51	PS 52	PS 53	AB 7	AB 8	AB 9	AB 10	HA 22

Assessment	AB 11	AB 12

Record of work: SHM 1

Shape

3D Shape	PS 54	PS 55

Position and movement

2D Shape	PS 56	PS 57

Measure

Length	PS 58	PS 59

Weight

Capacity

Time: days of the week

Time: telling the time	PS 60	AB 13	AB 14	AB 15

Data Handling

Sorting, matching, relationships	PS 5	PS 6	PS 7	AB 16	PS 61	AB 17	AB 18	PS 62	PS 63	PS 64

Bar graphs	PS 65	AB 19	AB 20	PS 66	AB 21	AB 22	AB 23

Round-up 1

1	2	3	4	5	6	7	8	9	10	11	12	13	14	15

Round-up 2

1	2	3	4	5	6	7	8	9	10	11	12

Heinemann is an imprint of Pearson Education Limited, a company incorporated in England and Wales, having its registered office at Edinburgh Gate, Harlow, Essex, CM20 2JE.
Registered company number: 872828
ISBN 978 0435 168759   © Scottish Primary Mathematics Group 1999.
First published 1999.   10   13
Designed and illustrated by Gecko Ltd.
Printed in Malaysia, (CTP-PPSB)

ISBN 978-0-435168-75-9
9 780435 168759